Music for a Medieval Castle

Between the 12th and 15th centuries many castles were built in Europe. They provided military strongholds and safe places for people to live. Here is a list of some of the people who lived and worked inside the castle walls. You will find music for them in the pages that follow.

The Lord of the castle.
His Knights and Footsoldiers.

The Lady of the castle.
Her lady companions and servants.

Servants in the kitchens.

Guests at a feast.

Minstrels.

Travelling entertainers.

Merchants and Crusaders.

The Lord of the Castle and his Knights and Footsoldiers

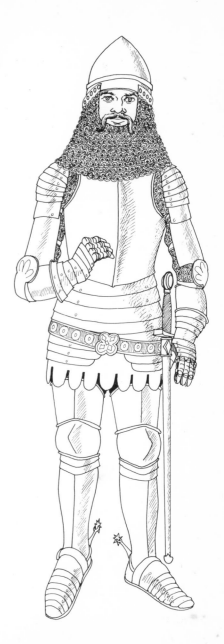

The most important person living in a medieval castle was the Lord.
Sometimes he owned the castle, and sometimes he held it for his King.
Next in importance were the Knights, men of good birth sworn to serve
their Lord. They had to be well trained and well fed if they were to fight
well; so each Knight had to have a strong war-horse to ride into battle and
a suit of armour to wear.

The armourers or smiths who made this armour were skilled men. They
made chain-mail armour from small metal rings linked together and plate
armour from sheets of metal hammered into shape on their anvils. Each
piece had to be carefully made to fit its wearer exactly.

Besides the Knights wearing armour and riding on horseback there were
Footsoldiers in the Lord's service. They wore stout leather jerkins and
carried spears, short swords, or the deadly long bow.

When the peasants working in the fields saw a band of armed men
approaching they must have been terrified. They knew their food and their
stores of corn and hay would be taken to feed the fighting men and their
horses. If it was a band of enemy soldiers their homes and their crops
would be burnt too. On the opposite page there is a famous medieval
song, *The Man in Armour,* which paints a grim picture of war in those
days.

1. Man in Armour

Man in arm - our, cru - el, grim, Death fol - lows him,

Death and fam - ine fol - low him. Blow the trump - ets, beat the

drums, See the man in arm - our comes, All read - y now for war!

Play A, B, then A again.

Tenor xylophone or **tenor recorder** play with the singers. Add a drum and anything you can think of to make a clanging sound like metal being hammered on an anvil. Use this rhythm

The music sounds more frightening if you play and sing it slowly and heavily. Mark the rhythm well.

Glockenspiel instead of xylophone for the B section would make a good contrast.

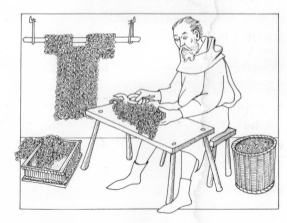

Ladies and Women Servants

The Lord's wife and the other ladies in the castle had a great many duties. They were responsible for the day-to-day running of the castle, with the help of a trusted headservant. The Lady held the castle keys and was in charge of the stores or supplies especially when the Lord and his knights and soldiers were absent. The women servants did the cooking and washing, and looked after the ladies' children.

After making sure that the servants in the kitchens, the stables and the courtyards were doing their work properly the ladies would sit in their boudoir. They worked together, making and mending clothes or weaving and embroidering tapestries for the castle walls. As they worked they sang songs and told stories.

Try making a wall tapestry. Instead of weaving, make a paper collage, each person working on their own section. Medieval tapestries often show knights and ladies among trees and flowers, hunting or hawking, or playing instruments or games of chess. Lap-dogs crouch on the grass together with hares and hounds, and birds of different kinds perch on the branches of trees.

Opposite you will find a song for the ladies to sing as they work.

2. A Song for the Ladies in the Castle

O gen - tle La - dy, no - ble and fair, (The hound lies sleep-ing, the fal-con has flown.) Shall

we go hunt the fine fal - low deer? (I love my love a - lone.) _____

Play A, B, then A again.

As an Introduction to the song play this drone on **violins**  or play its

rhythm as an E minor strum on **guitars** or **dulcimer**. Continue the drone throughout as an accompaniment.

Section B can be played on **descant recorders**. Add more verses of your own to the song, keeping to the question and answer pattern (*O I will hunt the fine fallow deer . . . If you will bring me a bridle of gold*). You could vary the accompaniment for each verse too.

A **glockenspiel** or **psaltery** ostinato

5

Servants in the Kitchen

Many of the servants in a medieval castle worked in the kitchens; and they had to work extra hard if the Lord had invited guests to a feast.

Imagine a medieval feast being prepared; men cutting up huge joints of meat, or making bread or pastry, women servants decorating sugary puddings (called 'subtleties') and filling enormous pies, chopping herbs, pounding spices, running to and fro from larder to cellars. Think of the leaping flames of the torches stuck in brackets on the walls, and of the great open fires, each with its iron spit on which the joints and fowls were turned to roast evenly by boys shielding their faces from the glowing logs. Kitchen boys or scullions cut up the food ready for the cooks who sweated with the heat and their haste to get everything ready in time. Pages had to carry the dishes to the Lord's table in the Hall in the correct order. Stewards had to see that each guest was properly waited upon, and everything done as it should be.

On the opposite page you will find some Kitchen Cries to help you make up a play about the hurry and bustle of a medieval kitchen.

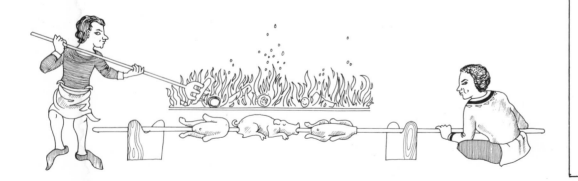

To make Marchpane Sweetmeats

Colour half a packet of marzipan pink, leaving the other half yellow. Mould the marzipan into little flower-shaped sweets, and finish each one off with a raisin or a small nut in the centre.

To cook a Pig

Take a pigge, draw him, smite off his head, cut him in iiij quarters, boil him till he be y-now (enough cooked), smite him in pieces and cast the syrop (the gravy) there-upon.

3. Kitchen Cries

Start with the spit boys and the scullions, to set the speed. Then add the pages, counting the dishes on their fingers. Then the thirsty cooks; then the anxious stewards, so that in the end everyone is speaking or singing at once.

Guests at a Feast

After the feast the Lord and his guests would dance. Here is a dance called a Basse Danse for you to try. It is a processional dance — the guests might dance it on their way into the hall for the feast.

Every knight and lady learned to dance well. Dancing gave them a chance to show off their fine clothes and their elegant manners. The steps had to be learned correctly and young people had to learn to move in a dignified manner. You will find this much easier to do if you make yourselves some medieval clothes like the ones in the picture.

 Listen to the shawm and the trumpet on the cassette. They were loud instruments used to play for dancing in a crowded castle hall. Basse Danse music was often based on the tune of a popular song of the day, as this one is. The tune was played slowly, and called the 'tenor'; the other musicians made up their own parts to go with it. Choose a group of singers to sing the tenor to 'Pah' or any other sound that makes their voices sound nasal and like a shawm. Place your musicians and singers up on a platform as if they were in a minstrels' gallery. Make sure the dancers begin and end their dance with a 'reverence' (low bow or curtsey) to the Lord and Lady.

4. A Basse Danse (based on 'Content Desir')

Play A, B, then A again, with the repeat. Voices sing the middle line to 'Pah'; their line is the most important, so use just one **descant** and one **tenor recorder** to accompany them. The **drum** is important too.

Minstrels

Here is some music to play while the dancers rest. Minstrels were musicians who lived in the castle and were part of the Lord's household. They entertained the Lord and his guests by playing and singing, and probably wore special clothes, perhaps with the Lord's coat of arms embroidered on them. A young boy learning to be a minstrel would have to work hard; the older men would be proud of their skill and strict with the boys.

A group of players and singers look much more like minstrels if they dress alike and if they play with their music on a table covered with a cloth, like tapestry. They could have purses hanging from their belts (for the tips they hope to earn) and decorated felt cases for their recorders. Make sure the audience realizes what skilled players the minstrels are, and that the boys in training (*apprentices*) behave as they should.

5. Up I arose, a Tune for Minstrels

You can see that the middle line of this music is much the most important. It can be played on **tenor recorders** or **xylophone**, or you could make up words and sing it with two recorders, on top and bottom lines, accompanying the voices.

Travelling Entertainers

Sometimes travelling entertainers arrived at the castle gates, hoping for shelter and food. The castle minstrels probably looked down their noses at them, and indeed their music was rather rough and ready. But they would know other ways to earn some food and a place by the fire. A medieval writer says they were able 'to play the drum, the cymbals and the hurdy-gurdy; to throw small apples and to catch knives; to perform tricks and to jump through four hoops'.

If you had to earn your supper by amusing people, what could you do? Turn cartwheels, do hand-springs? Tell a ghost story? Sing a comic song; dance, or mime? Medieval entertainers used to train bears, and even dogs and monkeys, to dance. On the opposite page is some music to accompany your performance. Train your musicians to play it just as *you* want it; slow for a bear, or frisky for a monkey, or with lots of fast drumming for acrobats.

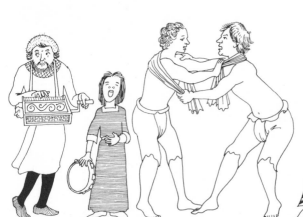

6. Music for Travelling Entertainers

Play A, B, then A again.

Violins This tune suits violins well, so it is bowed for you, or **descant recorders** could play it.

Guitars or **dulcimer** Play an E minor strum throughout.

Percussion Choose light or heavy instruments to suit the performers you
are playing for (a large drum for a bear, perhaps, or cymbals for acrobats).
Help to make their act as exciting as possible by the way you play.

Xylophone, Glockenspiel, Psaltery Add a heavy or a light ostinato on Es and Bs.

Beginner violins This drone is easy to learn by heart. Remember to repeat A to finish.

Merchants and Crusaders

When the Lord and his knights returned home after fighting in foreign lands they would bring with them treasures stolen from their enemies. They also brought luxuries from foreign merchants.

If you were rich enough you could buy silken cloth, jewels, spices and perfumes from the merchants trading with North Africa; soft leather from Spain, and wines from France. Traders made long dangerous journeys to buy these precious goods and to bring them to the fairs held in large towns each year.

Many medieval knights from Western Europe travelled to Palestine to fight in the Holy Land as Crusaders. On their way they would journey through the countries bordering on the Mediterranean Sea: Spain, France, Italy, North Africa, the Greek Islands. They would see new sights, hear new sounds, eat unfamiliar food. Sometimes they brought home musical instruments such as lutes, shawms, stringed instruments played with bows and the small Arabic drums called nakers. These instruments became very popular.

The songs the Crusader knights heard on board ship or in the seaports must have come home with them too. They had to have good memories, because very little music was written down in those days apart from church music. In the *Sea-port song* opposite some of the 'foreign words' have become just nonsense words.

 Listen to the music of the shawm, nakers, lute and fiddle on Cassette 1. Which instrument would you have brought home with you from your travels? Which luxury would you hope to buy from a foreign merchant?

7. A Sea-port Song

Very slow, mock-solemn

Me, my-o me o Mar-tin caught a flea - o, He cooked it well, And then gave it to me - o.

Very fast

Dama, Dama, Dama, Dama, Bring me the wine - skin, flea, oh flea, Mar - tin, Mar - tin, Mar - tin, Mar - tin,

Mar - tin caught a flea - o. He caught a flea - o, He gave it to me - o.

15

Mar-tin, Mar-tin, Mar-tin, Mar-tin, Mar-tin caught a flea. Oh, Mar-tin caught a flea. My oh me!

Make a big contrast between the slow beginning and the quick section.
You could play the second line on an instrument, but the song sounds best sung in two parts, to the rhythm of a light drum.
Use your Arabic nakers, if you have made some.

A Medieval Christmas

Christmas was a time of great
feasting and merry-making in the
Middle Ages. People rejoiced in the
birth of Jesus, and they also kept
up some of the customs of a much
older pagan winter feast, such as
decorating the castle hall with holly
and ivy.

There was plenty of music and dancing as well as feasting and games. The earliest Christmas carols seem to have been sung and danced in a ring, and to have been called 'caroles'; a leader sang the verse and everyone joined in the chorus or 'burden'. The words usually included a phrase or two of Latin. Everyone would go to church, especially on Christmas Eve.

You could make up your own medieval Christmas play, as the town Guilds did in the Middle Ages. For the Shepherds with their pipes there is a carol on the next page, and on p. 21 a *Shepherds' Dance* which might make a good ending for the play. There are also two carols for singing and dancing (instructions on the cassette) and a carol for a church procession.

In a medieval Christmas play from Wakefield the shepherds grumble about the cold weather on the bare hillside as they watch over their sheep.

First Shepherd:
Lord, what these weathers are cold
And I am ill-wrap't!
My legs bend and fold
My fingers are chapp'd.

Second Shepherd:
Lord, these weathers are spiteful,
The wind it is keen!

Third Shepherd:
Now in dry, now in wet, now in snow, now in sleet
My shoes freeze to my feet.

They decide to pass the time with some music; one sings 'the tenory', one takes 'the treble so high' and the third takes 'the mean'. In our *Shepherds' Song* on page 20 the treble can be Descant 1, the mean Descant 2, and the voices the tenory.

Medieval church music was beautifully written out by hand on parchment, with a border of leaves, flowers and birds. Sometimes the first letter of a hymn would be written very large and then a miniature picture painted inside it. Try this yourself, using felt pens in bright colours. What Bible story is illustrated in this letter?

+ Carols for Recorder (Touchin) nos, 34. 38, 39
983
1. Have you any other suggestions?
2. Would you like to try an original song?
8, 9, 10, 12

8. Out of your Sleep

A carol for dancing

1. Out of your sleep ___ a - rise ___ and wake! No - el, ___ No - el.
   Wak - en and sing, ___ for Je - sus sake! No - el, ___ No - el.

Now man is made of full great price, No - el, ___ No - el.

Now an - gels kneel to man's ser - vice, ___ No - el, ___ No - el.

2. *Now man is brighter than the sun, Noel, Noel,*
   For he was bought by Mary's Son, Noel, Noel.

   Now shall God bring both thee and me, Noel, Noel.
   Into His bliss eternally, Noel, Noel.

Glockenspiel or **psaltery** Play with the singers for the Burden, 'Noel, Noel'. The last line of the carol would make a good *Introduction.* This is a cheerful carol, so play it and sing it briskly for the dancers, especially the Burden 'Noels'.

Dance steps Notes on dancing caroles may be found in the Teacher's Book, Chapter 2, and pp. 22, 23. Adapt the steps to suit this music, or follow the suggestions on Cassette 2 if you prefer.

9. A Shepherds' Song

In dul - ci ju - bi - lo_____ God's will for man we show_____ Mer - ry may we

be ____ for soon our Sav - iour we shall see, And An - gels prais - es sing - ing shall set the bells a -

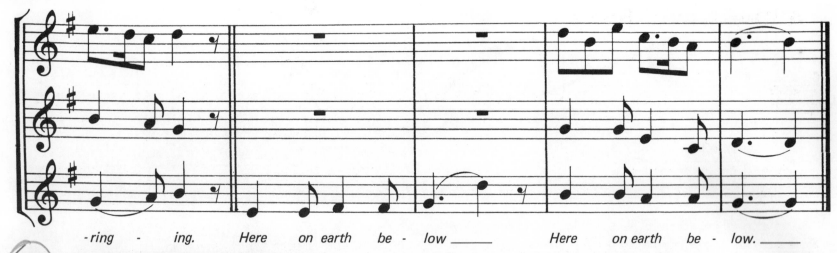

-ring - ing.   Here   on earth   be - low _____   Here   on earth   be - low. _____

10.   A Shepherds' Dance

In medieval pictures shepherds are often to be seen playing bagpipes, so you will want a strong 'bagpipe' drone with this tune. Use it as a 4-bar *Introduction* and throughout.

Violins could play open G and D in this rhythm as a drone, or use **guitars** or **dulcimer** on Gs and Ds in the same way.

Shepherds might have tapped a rhythm on their Tar Boxes too (tar was used as an ointment for sheep). You could imitate this sound on wood block or claves like this

What about the sound of the bells round the sheep's necks?

11. It fell upon the high midnight Another carol for dancing

Verse (solo) ... Burden (everyone)

1. It fell up-on the high mid-night, — Ei - a, No-el, No - el.
The stars they shone both clear and bright, — Ei - a, No-el, No - el.

Verse (solo) ... Burden (everyone)

The an - gels sang — with all their might, Ei - a, No-el, No - el.

2. *Three Kings there came with their presents,*
   Eia, Noel, Noel.
   Of Gold and Myrrh and Frankincense,
   Eia, Noel, Noel.
   As clerkes sing in their sequence,
   Eia, Noel, Noel.

3. *Now Jesus is that Childe's name,*
   Eia, Noel, Noel.
   And Mary mild she is his dame,
   Eia, Noel, Noel.
   And so our sorrow is turned to game,
   Eia, Noel, Noel.

A quieter carol, but you could dance to it too.
The Burden ('Eia, Noel, Noel') is the same each
time it comes. Here is an accompaniment to
play or sing beneath the Burden melody.

12. Make we Joy A carol for a church procession

Recorders

Voices

Make we joy now in this feast, Wel-come, Son of Mar - y. From a maid - en,

Queen of Heav-en Pu-er na-tus no-bis est. "Glo-ri-a" the an-gels say,

"Pu-er na-tus ho-di-e," Wel-come, Son of Mar-y. See the Son of

God on high Low-ly in a man-ger lie; Wel-come, Son of Mar-y.

Puer natus nobis est = A Son is born unto us. *Hodie* = Today.

This carol might be sung unaccompanied first as the procession approaches slowly, and then sung again with the 'descant' on recorders when everyone has assembled. Contrast between a solo voice and the full choir is also very effective.

Two Medieval Plays

Noah and the Flood
A Guild play based on a Bible story

Bell the Cat
A play about village life, based on
an old story

Noah and the Flood

If you were a boy living in a town your father might decide you ought to learn a skilled trade. You would become an apprentice to a baker, or a saddler, or a goldsmith, and he would belong to the Guild (or Society) of his craft or trade. Every year the Guilds joined together to act the stories of the Bible in the market place. Each Guild chose a Bible story suited to its trade.

The Water Leaders' and Drawers' Guild of Chester town was responsible for carrying fresh water to people's houses. They chose the story of Noah and the Flood.

Their play begins with the sound of thunder, lightning and rain. Then God speaks.

GOD   I, God, that all the world have wrought,
Heav'n and Earth, and all of nought,
I see my people in deed and thought
Are foully set in sin.
Man that I made I will destroy,
Beast, worm, and fowl to fly,
For on the Earth they me annoy,
The folk that is there-on,
Save Noah, my servant free,
That righteous man art as I see.

Noah thanks God for his mercy, takes note of His instructions for building the Ark, and sets to work, helped by his sons Shem, Ham and Japhet and their wives. You will find music to encourage them to work hard on the next page.

13. Music for the Building of the Ark

Descant recorders Play the tune briskly to encourage Noah's family as they work.

Violins Your part is the same for both sections of the tune.

Xylophones could play the same part as the violins; their woody sound is very suitable for carpentry.

Percussion Use wood blocks, light drums or claves to suggest hammering.

The same tune could be played as a March for the Animals as they enter the Ark. Choose your percussion to suit each animal (big drums and cymbals for lions and tigers, perhaps; or little bells for birds).

A warning rumble of thunder is heard just as the Ark is finished. God speaks again:

GOD   Noah, take now thy company
        Into the Ark, so speedily.
        And of all beasts and fowls take
        Two and two, mate and mate.
        Forty days and forty nights
        Rain shall fall for men's un-rights.

Noah and his family shepherd the animals and birds into the Ark. (*Another rumble of thunder*.) Noah's wife will not come in. She would not help with building the Ark and now she will not leave her gossips in the ale-house. In the end, her sons have to haul her aboard just as the storm begins in earnest.

Improvise some storm music. Let it grow from the first scattered rain-drops to the full fury of thunder, wind and rain.

When it dies away again Noah opens a window in the Ark and sends first a Raven and then a Dove to seek dry land. The Dove returns with an olive branch. Noah can leave the Ark safely, with his family and all the beasts and birds. The rainbow appears and God speaks once more:

GOD   Noah, I promise thee a behest
        That man, woman, fowl nor beast
        With water while the world shall last
        I will no more spill.
        My bow between thee and me
        In the firmament shall be
        My blessing now I give thee here
        Noah, my faithful servant dear.

Noah, his family and the animals sing 'God gives to us His Blessing here'.

14. God gives to us His Blessing here

A song for Noah's family

God gives to us His blessing here, His vengeance shall no more appear, For Noah is His son so dear, The rainbow is His sign so clear. Sing O my love, O my love, my love, my love, The rainbow is His sign so clear.

The tune might be played first on descant or tenor recorders while Noah and his family and the animals group themselves, ready to sing. Voices alone sound best for the verse, but the chorus (*Sing O my love*) is for everyone to sing and play joyfully.

Bell the Cat

The Parish Priest was an important person in a medieval village. If he was a wise and kindly man people told him their troubles and he tried to help them. Here is a play about a Priest and some angry villagers; they would probably be 'villeins', or farm workers. The play is based on a story from Aesop's Fables, one of the first books to be printed in England.

A Parish Priest sits alone by his fireside. There is a loud knocking at the door. In come some villeins. They are very angry about the way they are being treated by the Lord's Reeve, and his Bailiff. They complain about the Lord and his friends trampling on their crops while hunting, and about several other things too. Play the music on the next page while they talk to the Priest.

At last the Priest holds up his hand for silence. No doubt these wrongs must be put right, he says, but first they must listen to a story, an ancient Greek fable.

15. Who will Bell the Cat?

Music for the angry villeins

A Slow and heavy

Fine

B

Da Capo al Fine

Play A, B, then A again.

Make the music sound heavy and angry by playing it slowly and loudly as the villeins come in to tell the Priest about their wrongs. Play it on **descant** and **tenor recorders**; mark the rhythm with heavy **drum** beats, perhaps **cymbal** clashes too.

A heavy drone on **violins, guitars** or **dulcimer** will help to give it weight.

Suggested drone pattern

Use E minor chord on guitar or dulcimer, first finger E or B on violins.

There were once some rats and mice. They were troubled by a large cat, who stalked and chased and pounced upon them cruelly. On the next page you will find some music for the rats and mice to enter — scurrying, nibbling, and preening.

One night while the cat slept the rats and mice held a meeting: something must be done about the cat — but what? Then one clever rat hit on the idea of tying a bell round the cat's neck so that they would hear him coming and have time to escape. A fine idea, everyone agreed. 'But,' said a mouse, 'which one of us will be brave enough to tie the bell on the cat?' While they thought about this awkward problem the cat woke up and with one pounce sent them all squealing away in terror.

'So you see, my friends,' says the Priest, 'you will have to decide who shall bell the cat. Which one of you is brave enough to tell the Reeve, the Bailiff, and the Lord and his hunting friends that they must mend their ways?'.

The villeins scratch their heads and mutter excuses. This one has some ploughing to do, perhaps; that one has a sick wife to nurse; another one must see to his pigs. One by one they shamble away, and the Priest is left alone. He sits down again by the fire, thoughtfully. Presently his cat comes in quietly and, sitting beside him, begins to wash its face with its paws.

Each of the villeins who came to see the Priest should have a name and carry a tool of his trade (a ploughman's whip, or a sickle, or a shepherd's crook for example). He should think out carefully what his own grievance would be, and his own excuse for not making his complaint to the Lord himself. The cat and the rats and mice could wear masks.

Why was the Priest rather cautious about speaking up for the villeins? Perhaps he thought it would be best to speak quietly to the Lord about their wrongs when next he dined in the Lord's hall. Do you think the Lord would listen to the Priest and help the villeins?

16. Who will Bell the Cat?

Music for the rats and mice

Play A, B, then A again.

As the rats and mice enter play this tune as quickly and as lightly as you can, on descant recorders only. No drones, and only very light percussion. Break off suddenly when the cat appears.

Would the same tune played stealthily on a **tenor recorder** or **xylophone** suggest the cat stalking the mice and rats? Or would a single **drum** do this better, playing slowly and softly as the cat stalks his prey and loudly as he pounces? When the rats and mice gather again to talk over their problem play their music once more as they creep out of their holes.